On the water
Creative writing from Southampton

Published by Solent Press
Southampton Solent University 2017

Writers
Carina Buckley
Flavio de Oliveira
Rachel Di Nucci
Kristianne Drake
Ulrike Duran Bravo
Peter Hitchen
Emma Honeybun
Dave Hubble
Georgia Jerrey
Josh Jones
Pam Jones
Laura Lamb
Susana Lemos
Elizabeth Mayfield
Sophie Mitchell
Madi Maxwell-Libby
Dan O'Farrell
Stephanie Ospina
William Palmer
Sian Phillips
George Pugh
Megan Sherman
Alex Thornber
Martin Tvenning
Ray Vicencio
Matt West
Bhinduka Yokalingham

Editors
Jessica Bentley
Rachel Di Nucci
Josh Jones
Lottie King
Kieran O'Connor
Poppy O'Brien
Katherine Orman
William Palmer
George Pugh
Martin Tvenning

General Editor
Matthew Cheeseman

Marketing
Bobby Newton
Claudia Wilson

Illustration
Patryk Wirenski

Welcome to *On the water*, a collection of creative writing published by Solent Press. All the pieces have a connection to Southampton, be it through the writer or the subject matter. We are proud to publish established poets and first-time writers side by side.

The book is a product of many collaborations, something which Southampton Solent University excels at: English students edited it in collaboration with Dr Matthew Cheeseman. The students designed it in collaboration with Go! Grafik who also collaborated with the illustrator, Patryk Wirenski. He's a Solent alumnus and the Artist-in-Residence for Illustration at the University. Solent Press, co-ordinated by Tom Fowler, marketed the book alongside students taking our innovative units for writers and journalists. In this way students and professionals are involved in every step of the book's production, from the initial idea to the final, physical copy.

Since the call went out last autumn we received over a 100 submissions from students, staff and people from the city. The editing teams read the submissions blind, without knowing who had written what. The resultant book is sequenced in a way that doesn't separate writing into categories like 'poetry' and 'prose', but takes the reader on a journey from the personal and the emotional to the abstract and factual. The pieces flow from one to the other in three sizes. It's our interpretation of being 'on the water'.

This book would not exist without the artists, writers and creatives of Southampton. Their writing is a journey through pain and joy, humour and tragedy, politics and purpose. Thank you for reading it with us.

Suzanne Dixon
Professor of Creative Enterprise
Southampton Solent University

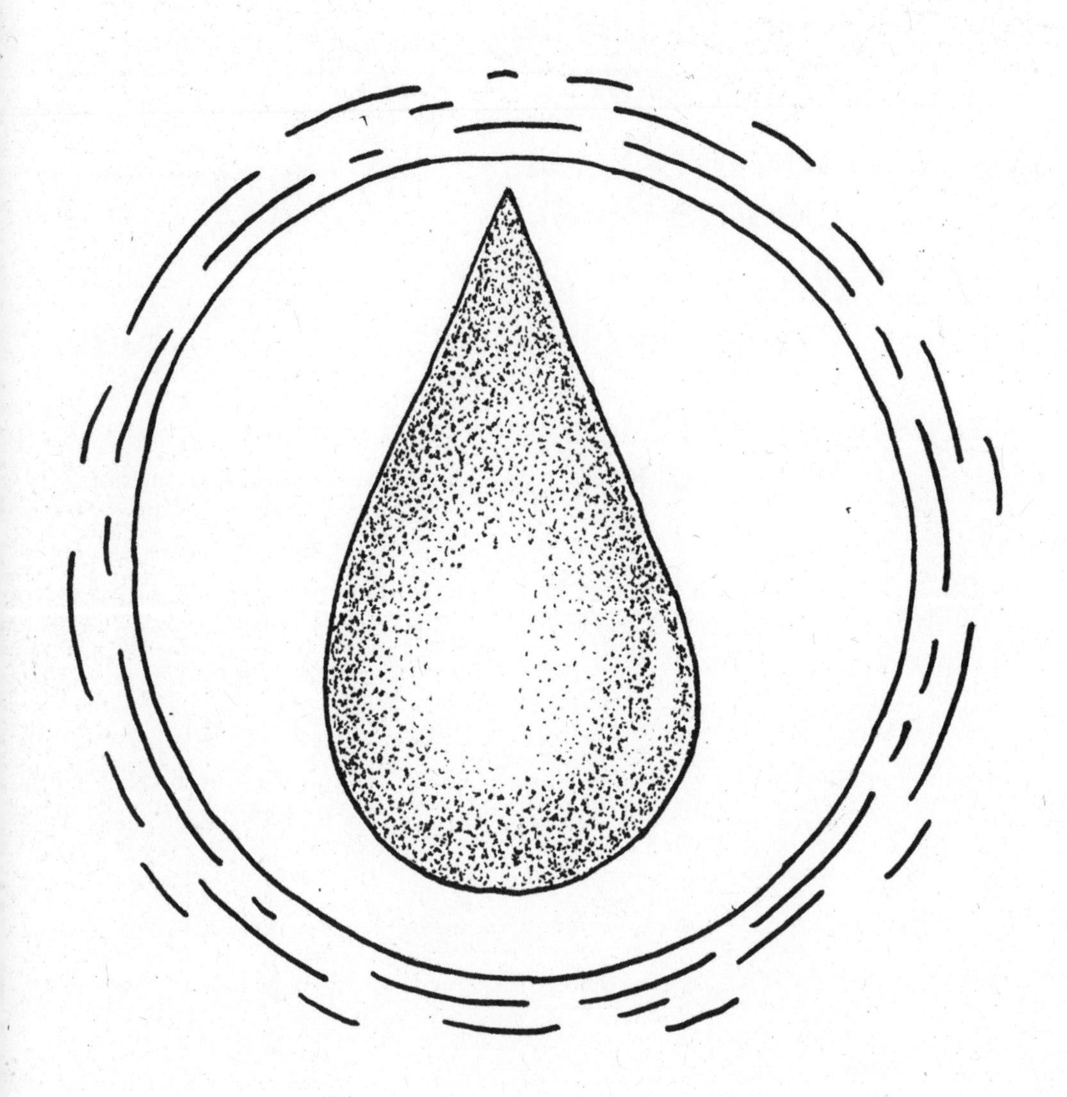

1 Kids, coins, cuts
Madi Maxwell-Libby

I took some kids on a summer camp
once
and in the front of the minibus, One
Direction's *You don't know you're
beautiful* came on the radio. A little
boy, about eight, was singing
along like;
'Baby you light up my world like
nobody else'
and I said, 'Wow, you know all the
words'
and he said, 'Yeah, I sing it to my
mum because she's sad all the time.'

This is for the children of Kids
Company,
a charity closed down by a thousand
toxic words
and its need rendered
invisible
by newspapers that preferred to print
in white.

It's for Jay,
feet sore from wearing
shoes that were too small.
It's for Ciara,
one pair of socks and no
she did not have spare.
It's for Rhiannon,
her mouth sticky with
Nutella'd squares of toast
at breakfast
because –
'yes I'm full but what if
there's no dinner?'
It's for Jordan,
who they found sleeping
under a car aged ten
and for Arley,
who when it came to
say goodbye
looked me in the eye with
eyes clotted
with tears and said,
'Please, please don't
make me go home.'

Meanwhile we're ruled by magicians
with scissors for hands,
economic illusionists, all coin tricks
in the dole queue;
'Now you see it, now you don't...'
Conjurors with cut-glass accents,
cutting counselling for kids who cut
to breathe,
Marks like braille on their body
speaking volumes,
cutting beds for teenagers with
lodgers in their heads
cutting EMA, cutting JSA,
cutting us short from the back and
on all sides.

'Money can't buy you happiness,'
say the ring-masters of the ring-
fencing pretence.
Spare me this — the idiom of those
rich in denial or not in debt,
who don't know what it's like to see
a parent smash a piggy-bank for
pennies when the wolf is at the door
and know that it will blow your house
down when it bounds in uninvited,

sniffling around for something to flog
to buy you another two weeks
on a future that is already in arrears.
And no, it didn't bring a bottle,
it didn't bring a gift,
it came to tell you that your time's up.
You're maxed out.
You're spent.

But we don't have to buy this sleight
of hand, we can call their bluff.
When we take a Churchillian
approach to children;
'Fight them on the beaches,'
watch their small bodies pile up like
sick, sodden sandcastles.

When the meek will not inherit the
earth
because they are not seen
and they are not heard,
and when money makes the world
go square,
so it's easier to hide cash
in its corners,
perhaps

the most radical,
the most powerful
thing we can say is:

'I'll take care of you.' ✖

2 The odd couple
Sian Phillips

'Did you see it?'
'Oy, Merrick! Merrick!'
'What's wrong with his face?'

The annoying click of multiple smartphones as they were held up in an attempt to capture his image. Stares that wouldn't let up, but continued to be planted on his warped, atypical face in an uncomfortable silence.

All of this had happened to Simon.

Indeed, all of these things had happened to Simon today, and it wasn't even lunchtime yet. He hunched over his egg and chips, his eyes downcast and liberally poured ketchup over his food. He liked this cafe; it had a cramped homely feel, with consistently good and greasy breakfast treats.

He was glad of the fact it was tucked away from the main high street and the ever-prying eyes. He liked it so much that he could even ignore the way the server had stared at him, eyes bulging and his Adam's apple thumping against his neck. It's not like that was anything new.

He lifted his scalding drink to his lips and almost promptly dropped it when the café door was wrenched open, clanging painfully against the wall, and a woman came in cursing under her breath. He kept his head down, wincing as she stopped in front of him, seeing a multitude of bags at her feet.

'Mind if I sit here?' she rasped painfully, clutching her hip and struggling to regulate her breathing. Simon's natural feeling of dread set quickly into his stomach, and he wondered why, in a café full of empty seats, she wanted to sit with him.

He slowly looked up, and nodded to her, 'Yeah, that's fine.' She was an older woman; hair dishevelled and make-up chaotically smeared rather than carefully applied to her face. She smelled of cigarettes but Simon found that he didn't mind this. It was oddly comforting.

She blinked once as she looked at him and nodded firmly; she lifted her multitude of bags and placed some on the empty seats that only displayed remnants of spilled sugar. 'Right.'

She limped her way over to the counter and Simon could only watch after her, marvelling slightly at her lack of a reaction. She almost seemed impervious to the one thing that always caused a reaction of some sort, through every day of Simon's 29 years.

This was new. His silent reverie however, was disrupted by an impatient glance from the woman now being served at the counter.

'I said, do you want anything?' she called out, rolling her eyes at him and shaking a head with a rueful smile.

'No, no, I'm good,' he said back, his voice barely raised for fear of drawing unnecessary attention. She shuffled back over with a cup and saucer in hand, clumsily spilling some of her drink so it formed a muddy puddle in the saucer. Simon made a face but noticed that she barely seemed to care, only swiping a finger into the liquid and sucking at it with a smile.

'I'm Jean,' she said, forcing a hand in front of Simon's face with hopeful enthusiasm. He looked at her somewhat cautiously before he accepted the invitational greeting. He wiped his damp palm on his jeans and took her hand in his, a friendly shake exchanged between them.

'Simon.'

She smoothed her hand over his gently before letting go; a genuine smile painted across her features.

'Well,' she said, taking a quick slurp of her tea. 'It's nice to meet you, Simon.' ✖

3 It was dark that night… Kristianne Drake

It was dark that night…
It was dark that night
But still and warm
And silent outside

It was dark that night

We were all in the pub
Celebrating my birthday
It was dark that night
I had no cares in the world
I didn't know you

It was dark that night
We all laughed
You were quiet

It was dark that night
We were all drinking
You were not

It was dark that night
We were all drinking

9

You started drinking and said

It was dark that night
You spoke
I laughed not knowing what

It was dark that night
So dark
So very very dark

It was dark that night
We walked as a group
Someone got lost

It was dark that night
You offered to go with me

what happens will be my fault

you meant

And find them

It was dark that night
I was drunk
We looked and called into

It was dark that night
You grabbed hold of my
‘I can do whatever I want and

It was dark that night
So very dark
I pulled away and ran

I ran
I ran

the silence

arms and said
no one will hear you out here’

I ran
My heart pounded
I ran
I ran
I ran
It was dark that night

It was dark that night
I saw house lights
I felt safe

It was dark that night
As I ran in through the doors
You asked what happened

It was dark that night

I told you all to shut the door
When he arrived and banged
It was dark that night
You let him in
I was terrified
Before I said a word he said
'It's not true, whatever she

It was dark that night
You all broke me
You didn't exactly call me a

It was dark that night
When you all pointed out
My words could have con-

I said ‘Don’t let him in’

says it’s not true’

liar

sequences

It was dark that night
Over twenty years ago
I put it into a small box

It was dark that night
When you violated me
You are darkness

I walk in the dark now
I look over my shoulder
The fear there, the memory
suppressed

It was dark that night
It was so dark that night
So dark. ✖

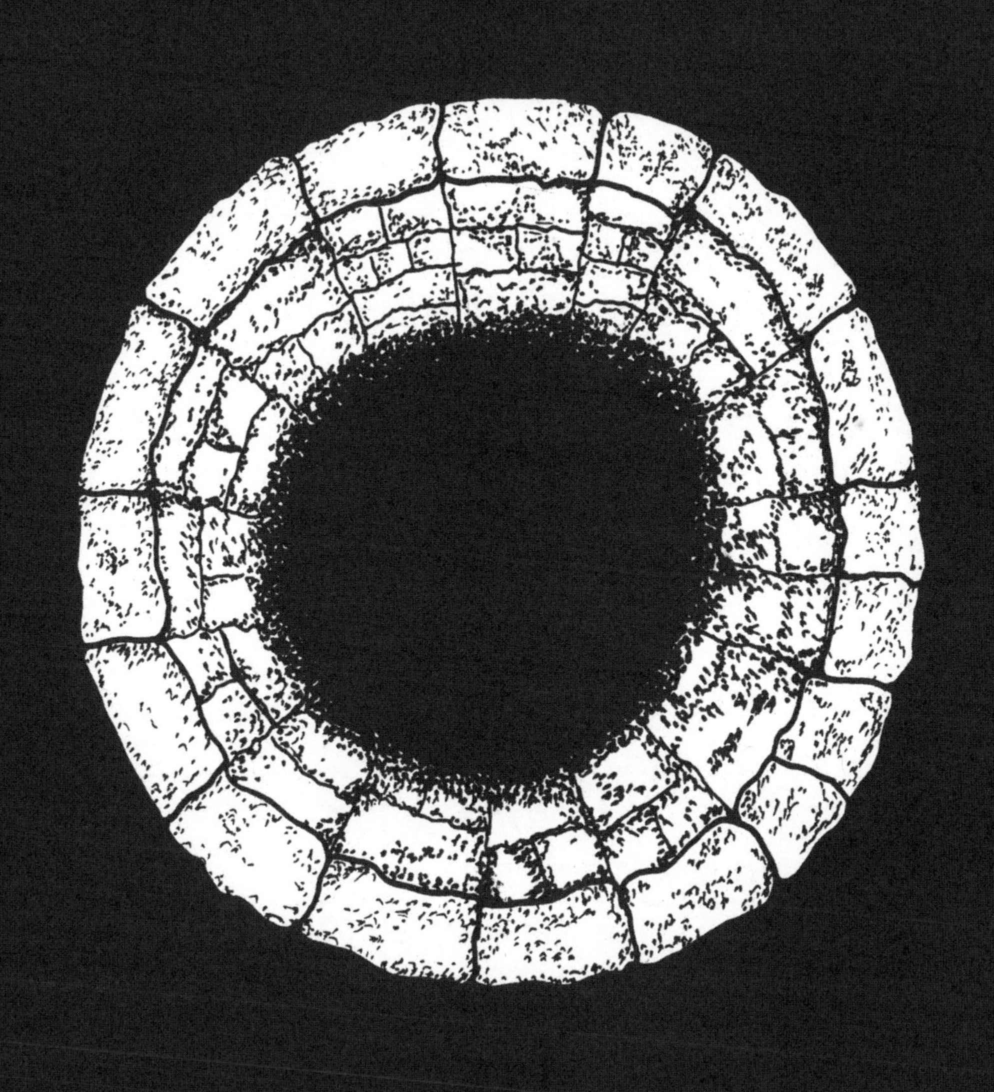

4 A repeat of the last year
Elizabeth Mayfield

Taking photos in your hallway, as I waited to run away,
Won't it be awful when you realise I'm everything you dreamed I'd be?
When you find all the folded corners in books I read whilst you slept,
And realise that between Fleetwood Mac and Art Brut all we did was break your housemate's wall.
The plaster as untouched snow on the stairs,
the faint make-up mark I made on the floor in your empty house
under the skylight for the last time you walked out in the rain
and I ran in heels over wet leaves with your keys around my neck
and we jumped in the taxi and got a train to anywhere, anywhere, elsewhere.

I left a bit of you behind in the place with the bare brick walls.

I went back to find it and came away with something else entirely,
and as I wake and disappear and drive and drink in an unforgiving tidal pattern unrelated to time
I realise I took not what I left in the bar, but what you did
and I am trying to make myself live on by making my year into puppet food for whoever we dismissed.

We can move your bed if that might make you comfortable. ✖

5 It's always better somewhere else
Josh Jones

The morning before I left was spent not letting the thought of uncertainty dig deep in our heads, but pouring boiling water on those worms until they were cast out of the gardens in our skulls. We pursued them with fiery determination to submit ourselves to hedonism.

We explored each other's bodies and shared laughter at the lack of discomfort in our sheets. We had beers with breakfast, filled the room with the sound of laughter and music and food cooking in the kitchen. The Holy Trinity of beautiful noise. I wish every morning could be like this.

I sometimes have to convince myself it happened and you are not some hellish trick I've played upon myself. Maybe it's just sentimentality, maybe it's just starlight, but now I know there is a life worth living in cities I've only had a short time to love, it's so much harder to go back to a home I don't belong to.

We barely said a word when we woke. Got showered and dressed in silence that hung in the air as the ropes holding us together became more and more taut. On the bus we didn't speak still, but you rested your head on my shoulder and watched the world I had come to love slip away from me. I wondered in that moment what you were thinking, wanting to know if you'd miss me. I guess I was being stupid.

I remember we kissed for the last time at the airport. While we made tender movements with our mouths, the ropes holding us together became tighter and tighter, then snapped. ✖

6 The Araucaria trees that look over us
Ulrike Duran Bravo

Some days my mother would wrap me in crocheted blankets and take me out into the merciless southern hemisphere heat. She carried me in her arms and showed me the world. I saw the blue sky and the white clouds above the mountains towering over the city. She pointed out the purple flowers between the green leaves of the jacaranda tree and the red blossoms of the Copihue bush. She said, 'Can you hear that little bird singing?' or, 'Look at that horse and its carriage', mimicking the clip clop of its hooves with her tongue.

'When you are older, my sweet Cecilia, I'll teach you how to ride a horse as men do.' It sounded like a promise.

I heard the engine and smelled the exhaust of a motorised car. My mother coughed at the black cloud it left behind. It wasn't common in those days. I smelled the dusty earth just before the rain came. I saw the white clouds turn grey and felt the drops on my brow. Often, after an hour or so, my mother would hurry back to the house, perhaps stopping in the bakery first where the rosy-cheeked assistants would crane their necks to coo at me and pinch my face.

Back in the room she'd lie me down on the unmade bed, unwrapping the pastry from its paper bag to feast on it, sending crumbs flying. I didn't give her much time to clean the floor. I could smell her milk and I wanted some, so I cried and she left the crumbs swept up in a pile in the corner and came to me. The ants came to visit us not long after.

I circle those first weeks of my life endlessly; that is where I spend most of my time. Lying beside my warm, soft mother who nursed me. She slept by my side all night and sometimes by day. Often I would lie awake simply blinking. Looking around the shadows in the little room; the wooden boards, the frames on the uneven walls, holding pictures that were not hers. By daybreak the blistering sun came fingering through the drab curtains to draw lines of white on the closed door.

My father was there too, mainly in the evenings and at night. He would come with food — avocados, tomatoes, potatoes, maize and olives. She'd leave me with him then, and he'd talk to me about the place they had come from, the place we'd return to — the blue ocean he'd show me with its white salt spray, the chickens they were planning to keep and the tall Araucaria trees that would look over us. He'd hold me, rock me and tell me not to cry, while my mother bathed or cooked or whatever other reason she had not to be with me.

I cried until the energy left me and the mucus blocked my lungs and the fever burnt my blood. My mother's milk was not enough. The doctor came too late. He said, watch her, keep her hydrated, undress her. In their desperation, my parents went to see a *Machi*, a *Mapuche* healer. She arrived with strange-sounding herbs to cook in water, the vapour to clear the mucus. But it was too late.

'Why? What did I do wrong?' my mother would ask me and I would blink. 'Was it the rain? Was it the sun? What was it? What can I do?' I would try to cry but let out only a whispering squawk and blink at her again.

She cried out for her own mother, 'Mamá, mamá help me, I need you here now, what do I do to save my little girl?' But her mother never came. She also cried for her Father, her Lord, and her God. 'Please Lord, I know I have sinned and displeased you, but I'll try to make amends. Please forgive my sins, my trespasses...' At night she would recite the Lord's Prayer and Hail Mary, gripping her rosary beads. But she also prayed to *Pacha Mamá* and *Ñenemapun*.

I left at night, after my mother had dozed off beside me having watched over me for hours and hours. When she woke with the sunlight, she found me staring at her, unblinking, accusingly. She reached out and felt my rigid little body. Her breath grew short and her eyes white with panic while she tried to shake me awake. 'No no no... Cecilia. Wake up, wake up, my sweet. My baby. No no no no no...' She offered me her breast. Perhaps she thought the smell of her milk would make me come back.

She did not feel my father's touch on her arm while she was trying to wake me. She did not feel his tears through the material of her nightgown. They wept in unison, though each alone. She held me tight, so tight, never letting me go, stroking my black hair, holding my tiny fingers, fondling my minute toenails. They had to unclasp her hands to take me from her. In a trance, she watched while they dressed me like a doll in the lacy dress she'd sown for a christening which hadn't happened. She watched as they put me in a box to take me away.

She sat in the dark room we had shared for ten weeks, sat and stared. Her hands felt her breasts that burnt with milk, now with no mouth searching for it. She lay down, tears and milk flowing, her dress soiled. The room closed in on her, her ears ringing with my cries, her heart cut open, all her sorrow flowing out of her, her hands numb from the cold body she'd been holding.They returned south, to the dark Patagonian rooms of her parents' house. Creaking floorboards and corners filled with Catholic shame that stuck like cobwebs. When my parents turned up on her doorstep alone, my grandmother asked, 'What happened?'

My mother replied, 'Pneumonia.'

She was unable to look her in the eyes. My grandmother was a stout lady, with a tough expression shrouded by a shawl of worry for appearances' sake. Searching her eyes you would find yourself caught up in the fear, in the guilt and the shame that she nurtured, like a fly in a spider's web. After looking at my mother for a long while, but ignoring my father, she said, 'It wasn't meant to be. Perhaps it's better that way.'

It was the closest anyone came to talking about me. My name was never mentioned, except when my mother was alone. Then she would softly whisper 'Cecilia' in a moment of loneliness, and I came to her. She told me many things. She told me about her wedding. It was in November: springtime. She had been carrying me for six months already and the loose dresses could no longer hide her bump. She told me she cried after her wedding. It was not what she imagined the day would be like. 'I hadn't hoped for splendour', she had said, 'but something better than a hush-hush formality in my parents' living room'. The wooden Madonna had watched them from her altar on the mantelpiece, her face reflected in the ornate mirrors hanging on the walls. Her black eyes followed them from every corner of the room. Looking at the dark cross on the yellowing walls, my mother fondled her own gold cross resting in the indentation below her neck. With her other hand, she clung tightly to her lover's arm, grateful for his presence. The clock struck three. It was the afternoon but it seemed like night: the window shutters were firmly closed so no one could look in. Only slithers of daylight entered through cracks, like mice. The room was lit with pillar candles and a couple of oil lamps. The registrar read the marriage protocol in a monotonous tone.

There was more bounce in his voice when the payment was being arranged, but now he was rushing through the formalities as if it were none of his business. 'I declare you married in the eyes of the law,' he said. 'The married couple should sign here,' he told them pointing at the place on the scroll with a pen, 'and the witnesses here.' The clock struck a quarter-past three.

The ceremony was over. A sigh of relief seemed to heave through the room. Both sets of parents had been standing at the back, but now my mother's mother came out of the shadow, guiding the registrar from the house. He'd refused her offer to stay for afternoon tea. The shutters were opened and my father offered his new wife a bouquet of pink roses, so delicate they were almost translucent in the new-found light.

The last time I saw my mother, she was on the roof of the airy house they had moved to when the family expanded. Apart from the new children and pets, she filled the house with dolls of different shapes and colours, each sitting between vases of flowers from her garden. It was the dolls that had given away her secret to the intuitive *Mapuche* nanny she had once employed when the boys were young. When she heard herself say 'We are a Catholic family and I am not about to fill my house with witchcraft,' she could sense the austerity of her own mother echoing in her voice. But the nanny often made up incense from the mountain herbs, filling the house with peppery fumes meant to clear the air of any harmful spirits. She also made the boys tremble in fear and delight with her stories of child-ghosts that guide the unaware into traps, and vampire bats that sucked the blood from horses and babies. They would always remember how the whites of her eyes glowed and how pointy her yellow teeth were in her wide open mouth when she cackled.

But my mother's thoughts were on her daily chores as she cleaned out the leaves that had been blocking the drain. With her white hair tied back, her face was as relaxed as the old shoes she was wearing, their soles split and the leather cracking. She should have been wearing gloves but her hands were dry in any case, her fingernails ragged.

She looked across the tiles of the roof and over the garden. There were lilies growing, their long buds on the verge of opening. She would pick them once they'd opened and place them in a vase in the front room. Beyond the lilies, she saw a young girl run across the path, her smooth young legs brushed by long grass. 'Don't even think about stealing the eggs from the chicken coop,' she wanted to shout, but then her heart clenched slightly.

Frowning, she dug her hands into the squelching mulch and threw the leaves into the blue plastic bucket attached to the ladder. She would return to Santiago, she thought, and plant a rose bush on her daughter's grave. Wiping her hands on her apron, she squinted across the garden again, wondering which of her grandchildren it was before she recognised me. She felt a stab in her heart as a mother does when her baby cries for her and then her heart simply stopped beating. Her body slumped forward onto the roof, her feet still resting on the ladder. The midday sun crept over the tiles and caressed her back as her soul left her body.

It was lunchtime when my father, his stomach rumbling, put his reading down and came out of the house to look for her. When she did not answer his calls, he walked round the house and that was when he found her bent over the guttering, unmoving. He climbed the ladder. He sat next to his dead wife on the rooftop for an hour, talking to her as if she was still alive, scolding her for not having taken enough precautions and that she should have asked him to do this job.

Later, he looked across to the end of the garden where the chickens clucked and then beyond the fields to the tall Araucaria trees that lined the foothills of the Andes. 'Well, Cecilia, she is with you now,' he said at last. It was the first time he had uttered my name in over forty years and it would be the last. ×

7 Last days of summer Martin Tvenning

Spending time with a

new-found friend
Enjoying the last days of
A dull sense of relaxation in
My shirt is stained by my
We are sitting by the ocean
Looking for a sense of calm.

The fisherman glances at his
Ignoring my friend,
She said the ocean made
But who wants to argue?
When it's the dying days of
She offers her newly bought
He accepts and eases the

I say nothing

summer.
the air
favourite kind of ice cream.

catch

her uncomfortable

summer
ice cream
tension in the air.

She says she doesn’t like
And thanks me for being her
We had only just met
To have dinner by the ocean.
She did her best thinking
Our smoke clouds rose high
We were closing in
The last days of summer
Sleeping in the tent,
I thanked her for being my
Conscious of the stain from

I moved our tent away from
Agreed that it was good that
Looking for a sense of calm
Our words into air. ✖

ice cream,
new-found friend

here
up into the air

new-found friend,
the ice cream.

the ocean.
she was my friend

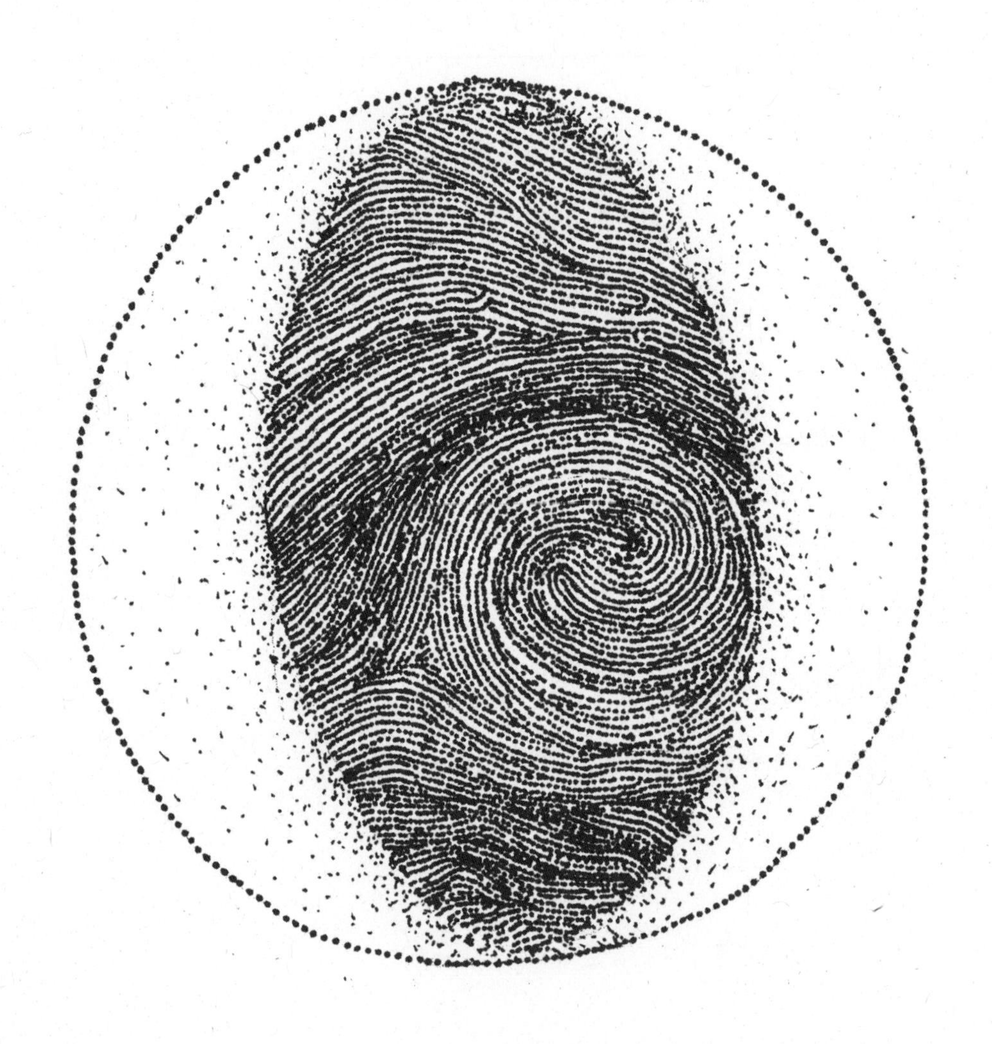

8 Mother tongue
Emma Honeybun

My dictionary says
You should be
Technically
Genetically
A biological parent:
Beget, origin, source — this is all.
Other meanings are erased for me.
That word that would have others believe in safety, and love
Now void of associations of nurture, tenderness, protector.
You chose to be Lady Macbeth, selling your milk for venom.
I didn't ask for this tongue, mother
But now I have this mother tongue
I'll play Caliban
And I'm sure as hell going to curse you.

You scorned me
For using the wrong word at the wrong time
An adult blaming a child for misusing a tool
Clumsy words not good enough
So I learnt that while sticks and stones may break bones
Words hurt too
And don't heal so quick.
So I determined to excel with words, to please you
But later you'd scold me for seeming supercilious, sycophantic
Nitt-picky and pedantic.

You made me obsessed;
My profit on it?
I'll use it to re-write you:
Not mummy — an emotional standing stone
But mummy — a rotting, outmoded monster, a dead sign
Words can hurt — but can heal, can rewrite:
You've become the cat's mother,
A womb, a matrix I've unplugged from.
Mome fool, blockhead,
madre scum,

modder dregs, decaying object,
mudde sludge.
I've replaced you:
Mother Nature, Mother Earth, Mother Goose.
Lose the mother but keep the tongue:
Language will be the motherland.
You were the mother of all migraines.
Mother didn't know best:
Mum's the word. ×

9 Ode to George Pugh

William Palmer

George Glyn Pugh,
What's two add two?
Because loving you is just
You've taught me how
To love with a scowl
And I love your beard cov-
And at the end of the day
When you come home and

as simple

ered dimples

say

‘Not you,’ I get weak knees
You’ve reeled me in
My most delicious sin
George, you’re the one for

10 Nine-oh-nine
Elizabeth Mayfield

The service announcement tells me that they're very sorry, but the nine-oh-nine train to Plymouth has been delayed. In school they taught me to never say sorry when addressing the public about a situation you know nothing about; it shows insincerity and annoys whoever is listening. I empathise with that now, and I'm pissed off at the announcement, thinking 'shit trains'. But when the voice continues to say the delay is caused by a trespass incident, this shortens to merely 'shit'. I wonder what the woman whose voice is blared out through loudspeakers across the country is like herself. I wonder if she's even alive, I wonder how she'd feel knowing her voice announced deaths a dozen times a day in the most loosely veiled code commuters know. I wonder how many hearts break a year to her voice. She announces the nine-twenty-five train to where you used to live and I figure out that perhaps everything she says has a certain tint of tragedy. ✖

11 Iridescent and light
Megan Sherman

It is a majestic evening,
iridescent and light
The witching hour is still as a stone
The moon ascends to her
celestial throne
A pearl in the sky, the divinest delight!
The starry climes brood over the sky
See! The cosmos is stirring, awake
And with its infinite movement make
The fluid Universe that flutters by

Dear Children, Dear Children, who in your happy dance
Appear untainted by the ways of men
Don't let the world turn you cold:
Seize divine fire all day, all year
God is speechless with love for your soul so bold
Which gets to go wild again and again.
✖

12 The phantom in the woods
Alex Thornber

In the beginning it had been merely rumour, the ravings of a drunkard, but slowly over time it had evolved into myth: there was something living in the giant tree situated at the centre of the woods.

Some said it was a gremlin, some swore it was a beautiful girl, one particularly wise woman thought it was whatever you wanted to see; a shape-shifting phantom with the power to read your deepest emotions. One thing every story had in common however, was that no one could ever actually profess to having witnessed it themselves, and those that did were almost instantly debunked as a fraud.

Many people would scout out the tree, hoping to catch a glimpse of this magnificent wonder. They all failed. It has been said that if you wanted it too badly it would never come to you. You are unworthy.

My mother would tell me these stories before bed. Her favourite — and mine — was one about a man her father had known. He had been so determined to see this beautiful creature, whatever it was, that he dedicated himself entirely to meditation in an effort to trick the spirit into thinking he wasn't thinking about it. He would sit under the tree and meditate for hours and hours to no avail. After a few days people from the village started to bring him food, concerned for his wellbeing. He ate nothing and refused to respond to his friends and family, so dedicated as he was to his cause.

But the spirit had noticed.

One day, the man's daughter walked into the forest to retrieve her shrivelled father, who was still sat cross-legged at the foot of the tree. She draped his arm around her shoulder and tried to drag him home. Despite his significantly withered frame, he was still too heavy for her, but she did not give up. I would ask my mother what happened next, and she would smile and say that all of a sudden specks of light and dust assembled themselves into human form under the man's other arm and he became lighter. The spirit had appeared to help the young girl drag her father home, for she was the one who truly deserved a miracle.

When the girl told her father this miraculous story he wept, furious at his daughter for having seen what he had almost died trying to. The girl apologised, pleading with her father not to hate her, as she was only trying to save him. But the next morning when she went to him, he was dead. Everyone said it was because of the starvation and dehydration, but the girl knew, my mother would say, it was because of a broken heart.

Despite the stories, as a child I would run and play in those woods, away from the eyes of everyone we knew. It was my safe space. When I would come home I would regale my mother with my adventures and bravery; fighting jungle pirates, or making friends with bears and the like. She would always ask if I had met the spirit, and I always sadly admitted the truth that I had not.

That is, until one day.

I had come back to my hometown to visit my few remaining friends and to help my sister clean out mother's house. It was not fair to leave it all up to her. Cleaning through my childhood home confronted me not only with the ghost of who I used to be, but also the ghosts of my parents and friends; memories vividly replaying in front of my eyes like a holographic projection. I couldn't breathe, I couldn't stand still. I could feel my heart beating faster and faster. I walked out of the front door and into the woods with a clear focus.

I walked and I walked and I walked until I couldn't move my legs anymore and my heart had slowed down again, collapsing at the base of the giant tree ready to give up on everything. I stared up at the light passing through the gaps in the leaves, looking like stars shining brightly in the daytime, just as out of place as I was. Closing my eyes, I breathed in the cool clean air and swore I could feel the oxygen pulsing through my veins.

I hoped that when I opened my eyes I would have been trans ported to a different world, but something entirely unexpected had happened. A gentle breeze gathered specks of dust and light into the shape of a figure sitting next to me. I could feel its warmth as if it were a real person. Tears welled up in my eyes and, as what felt like an arm wrapped around my shoulder, I wept. I opened my eyes again, and sat next to me was the most beautiful girl I had ever seen. She kissed the tear off of my cheek and said 'Are you okay?'

I couldn't speak; it was almost as if she had flooded my consciousness. Was I hallucinating? Had I finally lost my mind? Where did this girl come from?

For a moment I just stared at her, feeling comforted by her presence.

When I finally managed to say hello she told me of her short lives, each just a flash of time built around an unforgettable experience. She told me about the time she helped a lost dog find his way home, the time she was a shelter for a young couple caught in a downpour and the time she helped a little girl drag her father home.

She asked me about my life and I told her everything. She took my hand in hers and kissed me gently on the lips. I had never felt anything like it before and I soon realised she was everything I had always been searching for. She made me stronger in myself, happier too. Just having her there, caring and listening, meant everything.

I took her hand in mine and asked her if she would come back with me. She just looked at me. I spent so long staring into her eyes, trying to figure out her answer that I got lost in them and forgot about everything else as I felt her hand slowly fading away forever. ×

13 Unheard voices Stephanie Ospina

BANG!
SHOTS FIRED
TAKE COVER!
There's hysteria,
children cry,
men and women
caught in a colossal —

Blood spilled
without any miscalculations,
a place once home
is now in the
shadows of the name.

A place unknown,
'in God we trust, so here we
Dressed in courage and
we take the first step

and it's just you and I,
sat next to each other, along
others we don't even know!

Hold on, scrap that.

go.'
bravery

with 200

The bigger question is
why is it always us against

It's pitch black now, no one
all that you can hear, are
reminiscing on the days

Soothing whispers rise
infuriated by the fact, the

BANG!
SHOTS FIRED
TAKE COVER. ✖

the world?

is talking
muffled cries,

above and I'm here shivering
system has no brain.

14 Let it go
Ray Vicencio

and I, just like the ocean, am
unknown to you:

crashing waves and paralytic sounds;
a perpetuating feeling of prison like
crowds.
yet the crowded ocean; like water, is
a necessity for me to be alive and well.
Free flowing, unadulterated madness,
tears that flow with no feeling,
and I, distraught of all things you;
you, yourself, are one with the sea.
and yet nothing,
not the waters of the earth,
not the sun the sky the moon or the
trees,
could ever possibly compare to
the continuity of
my secrecy
my shallowness
and my unprecedented gladness;
that I am nothing.
And just like the ocean and the waters
and the waves of blue
I am colourless, clear, yet righteous
and pure,
free of life
free of death
yet chained to an unconditional fear

that I am nothing
without you. ×

15 Speak out Bhinduka Yokalingham

You, standing there so
With your head bowed
To your scruffy shoes and
You grab your phone from a
Swipe on the screen.
You slither out a used tissue
You stare at the poster.
You look to your friends.
You get off at the platform.
'Mind the gap.'

absent-mindedly,
down
pink-pinched hands.
pocket.

from the sleeve of your jacket.

You close your eyes and
You flick a page of the
No words are read.
No words are heard. ✖

pretend to be asleep.
newspaper

16 Head in the oven
Josh Jones

My friends would sell themselves out
For a set of new wings
Or at least
Some new strings
To tune their guitars to the
Feeling of fresh scars
And they'll write songs about
Unnatural disasters and
People they adore
From the covers of books
Who have seen things we can
Only dream of
Because we don't have the money to
get there
And boys in bands who
Paint their faces in makeup and
Actually give a fuck

We're all just looking for noise
That masks our sensibilities
And the ringing in our ears
Barely scratching at the surface
I believed you were beautiful
Until the drugs made you weird
Your eyes got glazed and your smiles were wiped
Clean, a sickening sobriety
Built upon exhaustion
The boredom of things we once longed for
I thought to myself
I don't wanna be a part of this
This is a path I can't follow because
I don't want to worry about
Who is going to make it to
The age of forty
You'll know I'll be waiting
For you
At the other side of this hole
But I can't pull you out. ✖

17 Joe, driving through the night

Laura Lamb

Joe was tired. He'd been driving all night and he still didn't seem to be any closer to his destination. He'd taken the weekend off work for this trip but he had to be back on Monday morning for a meeting. At this rate, he'd reach the house and have to turn straight around again to make it back in time.

He couldn't figure out if he'd made a wrong turn — or several even — but his navigation system had never told him if he had. Other cars rushed by him on either side, blasting air against the side of his car, causing it to waver a little.

How long had it been since he last stopped for a break? Time seemed to roll into one continuous drone whenever he was on the road. His eyes were growing ever heavier and his legs ached from controlling the pedals beneath his feet. Perhaps it would be a good time to stop, just for a bit. Focusing on his new goal, he scanned the landscape for a service station, hoping for a strong cup of coffee and a flushable toilet.

He'd left his wife still sleeping in the bed they shared; he hoped to be back before she next awoke. Sliding the keys off their hook by the front door, he'd grabbed his prepared bag from the under stairs cupboard and flung it over his shoulder, stepping out into the darkness.

Finally, in the distance, a sign emerged. The rain began a soft pattering against the windshield as he steered the car off to the left. The sign read: 'Feeling tired? Why not take a break?' Joe rubbed his eyes, uncertain as to whether they were playing tricks on him, but the apparent mirage was in fact real. Behind the sign was a small wooden cabin, porch lights glimmering with promise. As the rain grew heavier, Joe retrieved his bag from the passenger seat and stepped under the shelter of the portico. Another sign, with fading painted roses on either side, greeted him: 'WELCOME BACK'.

The house looked occupied despite there being nothing else for miles in either direction, and no other vehicles in sight. It seemed best to knock first, in case they weren't expecting visitors at whatever hour of the night this was. His hands hurt from gripping the wheel for so long in the same position. Flexing them back and forth as though playing an imaginary piano, he lifted his left arm and rapped his knuckles against the thin windowpane. It rattled, bouncing back against his skin repeatedly. There was no answer, so he knocked again. This time, he heard shuffling from inside; a door squeaking open and shut somewhere, a chair in a scuffle with the floor. A face appeared in the window, and the door opened slowly.

'Come in! You're more than welcome, my friend. Welcome back, welcome back!' A shaggy-haired old man grinned a gappy smile at him from the doorway. The inviting glow behind him softened what would have normally been a somewhat unforgiving face, weathered by time and experience, or possibly just rotten weather.

Shaking the damp from his bones, Joe extended an arm to greet the man in a formal manner. The man forewent the seriousness of the situation and pulled him in for a close hug. 'Welcome back, welcome back!' he continued to mutter. Joe's chin rested lightly against the man's shoulder as they embraced.

'You'll have to excuse the mess, I'm afraid. It's been a while since we had visitors, and we weren't expecting you so soon, truth be told!' the man explained, shambling back inside with Joe under his arm.

Joe was confident he had never met this man before, but he didn't have the heart to explain this to him. The old guy looked so delighted to have company that it would be rude to shatter his joyfulness. An explanation could wait, Joe thought.

Inside, the cabin was wall to wall with frames, some empty, some containing photographs and paintings. The paintings looked strange, as though they had been created by someone using their 'wrong' hand. A fire crackled in the corner, and an implausibly comfortable-looking set of chairs faced its warmth. After driving for so many hours in a cramped car with nothing but the whirring fans for heat, Joe couldn't believe how picture-perfect this new setting was. He blinked for longer than a human should normally need to blink for, signaling his fatigue. By the time he opened his eyes again, he was sat in one of the armchairs, his face toasting in the fire's balmy climate. The man seemed to have been talking to him for some time, though he couldn't tell just how long. He was in the middle of a very in-depth anecdote about something or other and Joe felt bad that he hadn't been listening, given his hospitality.

The man paused. 'You look tired. Let me help you to your room.'

Joe tried to mumble an appreciative response, but only muffled sounds came out. Sleep was winning now.

Joe awoke early to the sounds of macaws screeching from down the hallway. It was such a stark contrast to the usual sounds that filled his mornings that it stirred him in an oddly reassuring way. Standing on two feet, he felt taller than before. He tried to retrace his steps, unable to remember how he had made it into bed. Something had changed about the cabin. Perhaps it was merely the daylight shining through paper-thin curtains but things felt different.

He tried to play back conversations with the old man from the night before, but his addled brain was unable to focus long enough to take much in. The next logical step was to head through to the front room, where he had almost fallen asleep by that glorious fire. Hoping to find the man there, he would thank him, get in his car, and be on his way.

There was no sign of the man. The only company was a television set, blaring loudly at him from where he thought the fireplace had been previously. Technicolour feathers flashed from the screen and a voice boomed out into the room, reverberating into the kitchen and bouncing off cupboard doors and hanging saucepans.

'Although much has been attempted in terms of conserving the macaw, most are now endangered and nearing extinction in the wild. Deforestation and illegal trapping has led to their decline…'

With a hazy mind Joe placed himself in front of the television. Mesmerised by the scenes of nature that flickered before his eyes, his thoughts wandered to a calm and distant place. A delicious smell wafted from the kitchen, sweet and enticing. Sensing a presence in the room, he turned his head to the doorway and saw a young woman, apron bunched up around her waist. In her hands, a tray of freshly baked muffins, wispy trails of warmth floating from their centres and up to the ceiling.

'Good morning, darling. How did you sleep?' The woman's voice drifted as sweetly towards him as the smells of baking that now occupied the room.

'Well, I think... thank you', he replied. He didn't feel as though he recognised her, and yet she seemed familiar. Resting the baking tray on a side table, she approached him, and gently kissed the top of his head. Returning towards the kitchen she looked back and smiled lovingly at him as he whispered her name: 'Madeleine'. The name toppled out naturally, as though he had been saying it for years. A warm, instinctive feeling in his gut signalled his fondness for her. Unfazed, he returned to his nature programme, settling further into the armchair.

He must have drifted off to sleep again, because he woke to monochrome credits rolling across the screen, indicating the end of a black and white movie. Stretching his limbs, he walked over to the windows to peer outside at the afternoon sun. The bad weather from the night before was all but imagined now. Light refracted against the intricate glass ornaments on the windowsill, dappling rainbows across the cabin's timber interior. A welcome breeze filtered through slight gaps in the front door, as though gesturing him outside. Obliging, Joe unhooked the door's latch and stepped out onto the porch, sun beating down against his skin. There was Madeleine in a chair, sleeping peacefully. A large brimmed hat was pulled down, sheltering her face from the heat.

She stirred as he stared out at the endless rows of brilliant yellow flowers surrounding the cabin. 'I had a strange dream', she muttered drowsily. 'You were driving down a long road at night in the worst weather. I was watching you from somewhere else, though I'm not sure where. I was worried you might fall asleep and crash your car. But you didn't, you found your way back here to me, unharmed.' She lifted her hat and gazed lovingly into his eyes, her brown flecks meeting his blue and yellow fragments.

'I'm going to stretch my legs. Is the town far from here?' Joe asked, feeling disorientated.

'You keep asking the way to go, Joe. It's so funny. I honestly don't know how you don't get lost between the bedroom and the living room sometimes', Madeleine replied, pointing to the horizon on their left. 'Can you pick up some fresh fruit for us to eat after dinner?'

Joe followed his legs into town.

'Hi, Joe!', a stranger exclaimed, waving from across the street. 'How's Madeleine feeling today? Any better?'

'She's doing fine, thank you', Joe found himself replying.

'Glad to hear it buddy!'

Everywhere he turned, friendly faces grinned at him or tipped their caps and nodded. Joe felt exhausted, despite having barely done anything more than sleep all day. Heading back across the butter-yellow fields, he swung a bag of apples back and forth in time with his pace. The shoes on his feet looked worn through, as though a rogue toe might burst forth any moment.

Wearily, he brushed through the final rows of weeds and flowers in front of the cabin and settled down on the front stoop. His gaze followed the wind scraping through the grass before him as it began to spit with rain. Growing steadily heavier, a sudden orchestra of clouds gathered above. Rapidly and all around him, small puddles formed. And there it was, his own face, on the ground below him, reflected back. The youthful complexion he

remembered as his was gone, a greying tussock of hair now rested on top of a confused and wrinkled expression. Wiry hairs poked out of his brow in all directions, chaotically. Shocked, he clutched at his aged skin, the mirrored version echoing him. This face that was now his, also belonged to another: the man who had kindly welcomed him the night before, into this sanctuary from the burgeoning storm.
The door behind him swung open, and Madeleine came into view in the expanding puddle at his feet. 'Oh Joseph, you silly old thing, you'll catch a cold out here! Come inside and dry off.'

But Joe remained still, staring at the watery scene playing out before him, a kind-eyed old woman miming Madeleine's words, her salt-and-pepper hair rippling back and forth against her face as the wind grew ever stronger. ×

18 I never caught her name
Dave Hubble

We're hunting whales,
not with harpoons,
but cameras,
clipboards and binoculars.
As we count, gauging age,
identifying sex and species,
a North Atlantic storm boils up,
tracks our way,
rain comes, sun dims,
we roll-pitch-yaw,
gimballed by the peaks and troughs
of swell —

all's well until the watchman,
pointing with a tremble,
warns 'great wave' –
we turn to see the dark horizon rise,
looming up to touch gunmetal sky.
Close hatches, stow deck-gear and tether,
we gather in the wheelhouse
where even seasoned salts
exchange a glance.
Slowly, our vessel lifts,
crests bow high, then dives through foam,
plunging deep as gannets,
the cut-and-shut ex-trawler
creaking under heavy water
as even mast-tips slip beneath the surface.
Hull twists and flexes,
welds and rivets strain
with pinks and pops of torsioned steel –
all other sounds have ceased,
muffled by the grasping wet;
breaths are held and then, as one, released,
the ship corks back up,

gasping, spilling brine
behind the passing beast,
and as light cracks the clouds
we are greeted by
the day's first blowhole spray. ✖

19 Romance
Sian Phillips

They were glad to be able to lie together; chest against chest, warm thigh against warm thigh. A rotating light moved slowly above them, illuminating their faces to each other and bathing them in a gentle glow. His eyes were trained on hers, wide and wondering, and she didn't flinch when his hand pressed lightly against her cheek. His fingers were lightly coated with food and they felt sticky against her skin, but this only caused her to smile. Her white teeth showed as she enjoyed his touch.

He shifted impossibly closer and brought their mouths together; increasingly wet, they exchanged fluids by pressing their lips against one another's. Clear liquid ran from his nose until she could taste it on her tongue, likely that a small infection would now pass between them, so close was their proximity.

The music softly playing in the room was interrupted by his coos of love and she was quick to reciprocate and join in chorus with him. The food from lunch was shared between them like birds, from her mouth to his. Both were sure it tasted better this way.

His eyes began to droop with each passing minute, sated by their meal and she marvelled as his eyes rolled back like a drunk's as he fell into a peaceful slumber. She stroked lightly at his cheek with splayed fingers, feeling the heat of his flushed cheek and hoping he didn't have to endure the hurt for much longer. She felt her own teeth with her tongue, and was glad that part of her life was over.

He could be selfish sometimes, she knew that. He would grab a desired item from her with a howling protest, and would cry if she refused to relinquish something to his firm grasp. He needed her to put him first and consider his needs, before she paid attention to her own. She knew that this would likely change with time.

She moved in closer and placed her head to his rising chest, feeling the steady thump of his heart. It wasn't always easy, but for right now, there was no separating two babies in love. ✖

20 In retrospect
Elizabeth Mayfield

Do you remember the night we drove out east? The sunset hit the trees but I wouldn't take my eyes off the road. I screamed, 'Look at it, look at the colours!' and squeezed your hand like I could experience the view through you.

Do you remember how you wouldn't let me leave unless I promised to come back in the evening? You taught me patience on the days you were busy, but you taught me to drive in the dark on the nights you were free. Sleeping obscurely on your couch whilst you smoked and I batted your hand away whenever you tried to wake me.

The day you hugged me forever and kissed me on the cheek, you said you'd see me soon. I promised to call in a few months, you reluctantly accepted it'd be that long. You didn't want to wait, but you didn't have a choice, because you didn't want me to stay that time either. ✖

21 Returns
Matt West

Tarquin puts the knife down
straightens his collar

folds napkin
rolls thick cotton

into White's
silvered holder.

Celery salt goes
back in the cellar.

The duty waiter takes
the plate to the kitchen

where chef unpicks ingredients
and shuts the fridge door.

Eggs go back in the pan
until speckled green in cooling water.

A polystyrene container
is sent to Reception

where Rebecca wipes her name
from the courier's list.

She hands him his clipboard.
He slams the door of his van

hurtles down the M3
to the M27

before turning at Lyndhurst
and cutting through the forest.

At Lymington he's met
an hour after sunrise.

On the darkening estuary
a dinghy steals out

holding a man wearing wellington boots
and an oilskin jacket

who reaches a hand over
the Common Cord grass

and returns the eggs
to nest. ✖

22 Getting it together
Peter Hitchens

A pub darts and dominoes team.

Cast in order of appearance:

SPARTACUS	Fourteen year-old boy. Intelligent. Articulate. Club Secretary and de-facto leader.
BIG MICK	Mid forties. Cognitively challenged. Brilliant darts player.
BRIAN	Mid forties. Dominoes player.
GEOFF	Mid fifties. Darts player.
ALAN	Late fifties. 6’4”, eighteen stone. Balding shaved head, broken nose. Casually violent. Useless at both darts and dominoes.
GEORGE	Mid thirties. Career criminal. Recently released from Strangeways. Club Treasurer.
MOLLY	Mid sixties. Acid-tongued pub landlady. Spritely. Nobody’s fool.
OTHERS	Members of the darts and dominoes team.

In early 1980s Northern England Thatcherite anti-working-class discrimination and ideologically imposed austerity measures continue to exacerbate the privations faced by the already impoverished.

The action, lit by early-morning sunshine, takes place in a dingy pub vault on the outskirts of a town. A large bay window at right angles to the bar overlooks a shabby, part-cobbled car park beyond which is a deserted dual carriageway. Inside, underneath the window, is a leatherette backrest that extends round into a chimney breast alcove. Fixed to the centre of it and directly opposite the bar is an almost obsolete dartboard; beneath is a shiny, branded, black vinyl runner protecting faded, cracked Linoleum tiles. The runner abuts an oche fixed a metre from the bar. On the wall next to the gents is a Yahtzee machine, it flashes intermittently and is occasionally audible. Diagonally opposite and out of reach is a TV sellotaped with a note warning 'Do not switch over'. There are several Formica-topped tables and various chairs and stools and little sense of space.

SPARTACUS: (Seated at the bay window table surrounded by the [mostly standing] men takes a letter from an envelope and begins to read). 'Dear Sirs, further to the events of the evening of 11 November. The brewery, following consultation with the landlord of The Miner's Lamp, holds you wholly, solely and collectively responsible for the damage caused to property, fixtures and fittings. As you may be aware, the cost of repairs is not inconsiderable; not least the replacement of the television set and the re-covering of the pool table. Please find enclosed our invoice, which we trust you will honour by return. Yours without prejudice, Messers Thicke and Long. Solicitors. For and on behalf of Greenall Whitley Brewery Company Ltd.' (Silence apart from the Yahtzee machine).

BIG MICK: Where did the pool table end up?

BRIAN: What d'you mean?

BIG MICK: Well, pool tables are 'eavy, I once tried to nick one from West Ward Labour Club. So how did it get out o't pub?

BRIAN: What are y' talkin' about Mick?

BIG MICK: What I'm sayin' is where did they recover it from.

BRIAN: Fuck me Mick, it didn't get recovered it got re-covered. (Big Mick appears confused).

So how much are they after Spartacus?
(Spartacus turns the letter over, then picks up the envelope and shakes a piece of paper out onto the table. Everyone gazes at it).

GEOFF: Four hundred quid! They've got to be jokin'. They've no chance.

ALAN: I don't know Geoff – it was a Sony Trinitron – the remote looked like something from NASA. It had picture-in-picture and everything.

GEOFF: It had a pool cue in it when I last saw it. I swear Alan, you looked like Fatima Whitbread. That was some shot my friend.

ALAN: Not really Geoff, I was aiming at that bastard who played the double nine for sixteen and the match.
(General laughter).

BIG MICK: Four hundred quid though...
(The enormity of their predicament starts to become apparent).

SPARTACUS: Okay. First thing. We're all in this together right? (Nodding and mumbled agreement from the men) So, next thing. How much is in the kitty?
(George pulls a grubby notebook from his Parka and inspects the entries).

GEORGE: Fuck all.
(A melee breaks out. It is silent and brief. Spartacus is uninvolved).

SPARTACUS: Can we all just calm down and work something out. Fucking hell.

ALAN: He's right. Sit down and shut up (pointing at Spartacus) and less swearing from you.
(Everyone sits down) So go on then college-boy.

SPARTACUS: Well first off George, no offence mate but how come there's no money in the club? We've all been paying subs since the start of the season so by my reckoning there should be hundred and eighty quid in it and that gets us almost halfway out the shit.
(All eyes turn to George).

GEORGE:	You're right Spartacus, that's what *should* be in the club, only... only I've had to have a bit of a borrow out of it now and again. I couldn't turn out for the team otherwise, y' know how it is, GIROS are next to nowt.
BIG MICK:	What's the point in 'avin a treasurer who's gonna rob the club?
	GEORGE (squares up to Big Mick): I said borrow, not keep. And if you ever call me a thief again I will kill y', so I'd shut up if I was you, Mick.
ALAN:	(stands up). George, sit down. Both of y', button it. Spartacus is gonna tell us what to do. Come on then Einstein let's hear it.
SPARTACUS:	One thing's for sure, arguing amongst ourselves isn't going to help. If George said borrow I believe him. (Spartacus fixes George with a gaze) So he'll pay it back. You'll pay the money back into the club won't you, George? As long as the money's back in the club by the end of the season, before anyone would actually get paid out anyway, then it's like it's never been gone in the first place.
	(This logic seems to win the men over. George is especially keen).
GEORGE:	Spartacus is right. I'll put the money back in time for the Manchester trip and everyone'll get paid out. Right?
SPARTACUS:	So all we need to do now is get the four hundred quid together. Sharpish.
BIG MICK:	Can't we just tell 'em to fuck off?
ALAN:	You should've been a diplomat, Mick.
GEOFF:	What, and get kicked out of the league halfway through our best season in livin' memory?
BRIAN:	Spartacus, you're gonna 'ave to write a letter. You're good at that sort of thing. Write and buy some time so the rest of us can get on with finding the sponies.
	(The landlady appears behind the bar).

MOLLY: Are any of you gentlemen actually going to buy a drink this mornin', it's nearly twelve o'clock, I open in half an hour.

GEORGE: (Attempting to be suave). Molly, might I say you look like a million dollars. Drinks all round and one for yourself. I'll get these. (Molly starts to pull the pints to the sound of cheering; George sidles over to Spartacus who is on his way to the gents. He puts his arm around the boy's shoulders and continues *sotto voce*). I've heard you're a handy little sod. Six fights, six wins and six KOs i'nt it? St Cuthbert's ABA must be well chuffed. Best run since Alan boxed for 'em and fuck knows that's a long time ago. So not only can yer throw a left and right but yer can read and write to boot. I think you and me need to 'av a little chat. ×

23 Your Facebook feed is not the world Dan O'Farrell

Your Facebook feed is not
Your Facebook feed is not
You've unfriended all the
the bigots and the churls,
so your Facebook feed is

the world,
the world
racists,

not the world.

You've blocked four friends
Britain First
& deleted Uncle Gerry...
for something even worse
& now you live in your
preaching to the choir
& everyone agrees about your
but outside on your
a fat man's set up stall
& is passing UKIP pamphlets
to ladies wearing shawls
& the newsagent on the
though the front page says
should be harpooned like
& the Muslim girl behind the
takes the money for this bile

from schooldays, for sharing

walled garden,

thoughts on Lars Von Trier…
pavement

corner's sold out the *Daily Mail*
that immigrants
whales
counter

from the queue of tutting
who cannot meet her eye...

So be careful out there, all
Your Facebook feed is not
Your iPhone screen is not
your iPhone screen is not
and if Dorian Gray took
would time still take its toll?
Your iPhone screen is not

& you've told the guys on
about how much you hate
& a celebrity retweeted you
on Arthur Askey's legs
& from where you're looking

pensioners

you loving boys and girls,
the world
your soul,
your soul
selfies,

your soul.

Twitter
Nick Clegg

it's a golden age for sure
a paradise in pixels, a
but somewhere in Malaysia
a worker staggers home
from sixteen hours making
that she will never own
& you want to smash the
by subverting from within
but you need more lives in
if you're ever gonna win
& somehow that distracts
like the peoples' heroin
but it's the methadone of
it's not even opium.
So be careful out there all
Your Facebook feed is not

utopia for all

smartphones

system

Candy Crush

you

the masses,

you loving boys and girls
the world. ✖

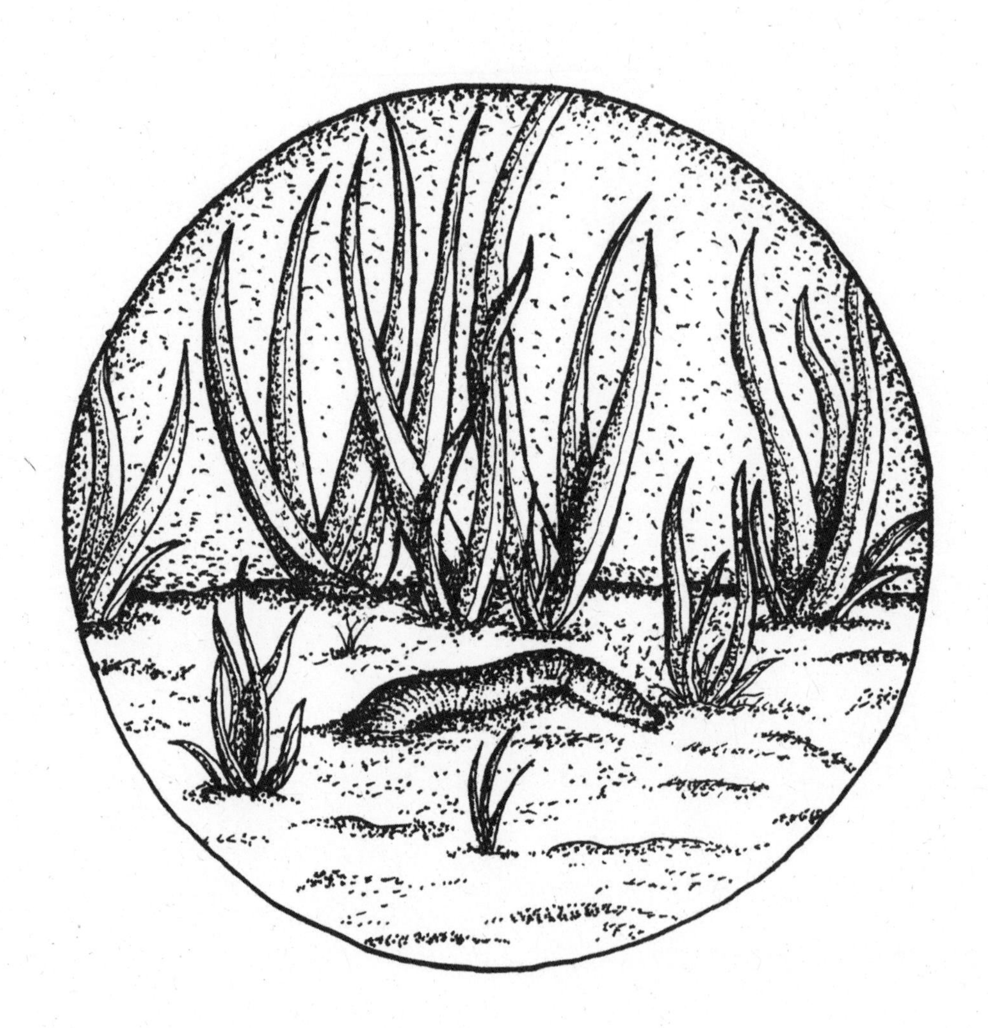

24 A drop of water
Patryk Wirenski

A drop of water, so rich with life
A finger print, just as unique
The eyes we look through
Accustomed to destruction

A worm, breaking the surface
Your hand picking it up
Only because you can

All that's naturally free
Will be unavoidably controlled

The thirst for destruction
The hunger for power
Never quenched or satisfied
We dig a well, never too big
Never too deep
Natural progress disrupted

With time the well
Will end up
Empty ✖

25 Being tall is not okay
Susana Lemos

I would like to say my life is perfect,
But it perfectly isn't.
It rages unwillingness.

Blasphemy,

I'm weeping for two: your mistakes and my forgiveness.

I feel claustrophobic within my own presence.

I try to save myself,
But the only thing I save is you,
everyday. ✖

26 Ghosts
Peter Hitchens

Inconclusive provenance bombsite bones
Bormann went to South America
but like an English car park king
DNA de-bunked the bunker myth.
Re-buried like Bergen-Belsen's bones
but they couldn't bury his ghost.

'Are ghosts really real daddy?'
'Ghosts? No there's no such thing.
Now close your eyes and go to sleep.'
Couldn't tell the truth now, could I?

So I denied Irving's Prussian Blue eyes
his examination, revision and lies and the
jack-boot air-ware white laces and white
braces. Didn't say about the web of white power
or of the fantasists with Death's Head avatars
dreaming of Valhalla; or of *username:C18*
trying to date *username:ZyclonB*.
Or of Breivik's sanity. Or the beer hall brawls in
Minehead and Margate or the pool hall cue balls
swung by screwballs in union socks.

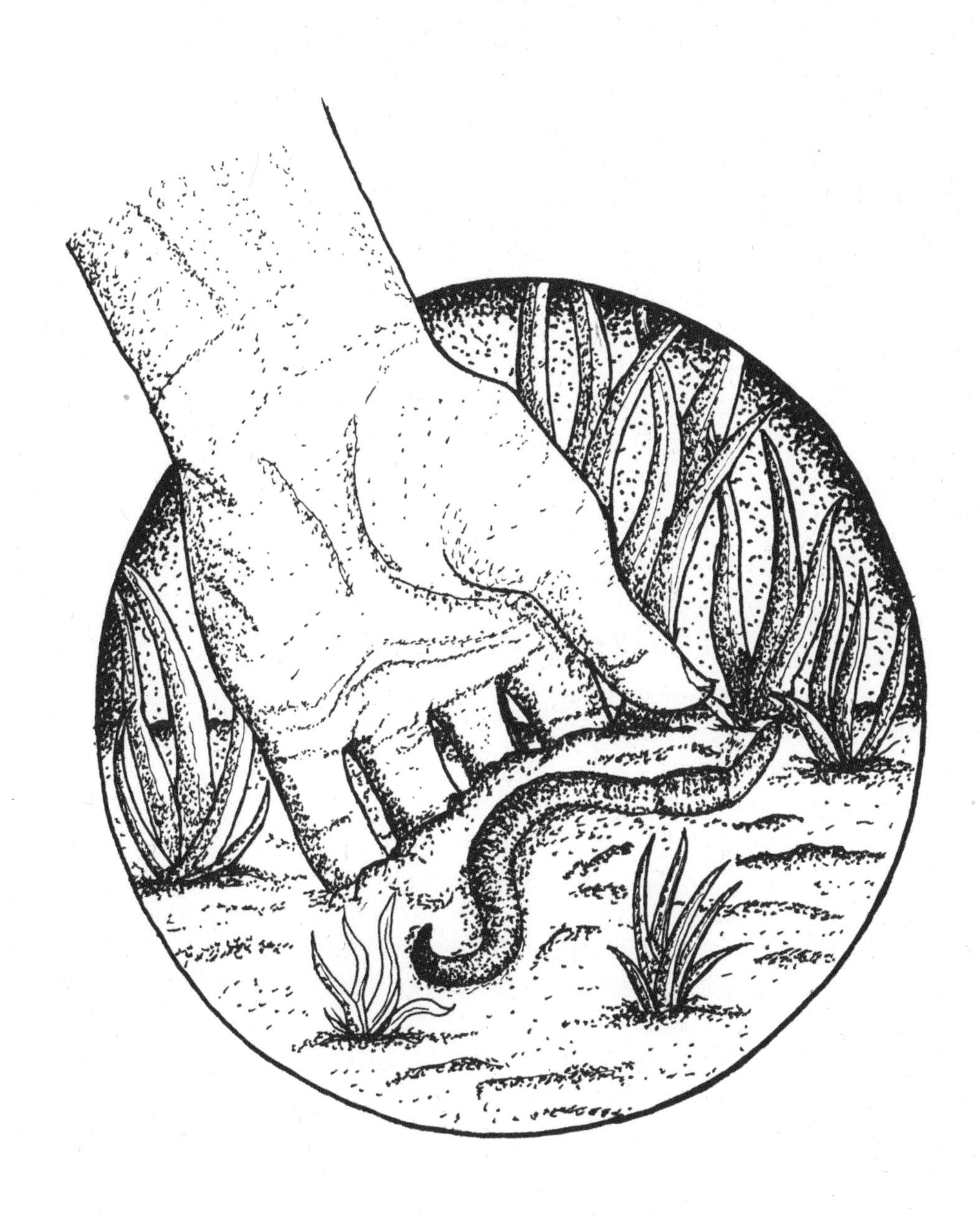

Didn't mention about British Bulldog in the playground
or the pit bulls in no man's land. Ignored the broken windows
in Bradford and Bolton and the broken grave yard
in Cheetham Hill and the barber's sign across the road;
'#1's £3 bullet creases free. Appointments not always necessary'
Didn't tell him about the pilfered portraits hanging
like other-era avatars on walls from Garmisch to Ghent.
Their new admirer's begetters knew ghosts couldn't speak.

'Ghosts? No there's no such thing.
Now close your eyes and go to sleep.' ✖

27 Indigestion
Carina Buckley

Salvatore Garcia Perez was a cook. That is to say he was alive – to him the two states were equal and indistinguishable. The queue, a dozen deep, was his artery; the hot blue of the gas burner his flaming heart, the spices in the air oxygen itself. His very soul was edible.

With an eye born of fifteen years' experience, he added another habanero to the chilli. The orders came up; the food went down. One smoky pork taco and refried beans, steaming beneath its waxed cardboard lid and passed into eager hands. A stir to the chilli before it anointed the portion of red rice and was itself crowned with a satisfying dollop of his special yoghurt sauce. A gift, a favour, a blessing to the young man with bright eyes waiting below the hatch.

He would be back. They all come back.

The next group in line were regular Saturday night pilgrims and Salvatore knew what they would order, what they needed from him. This one here with the beard always chose fish, so tonight he would order the fish tacos. And it was so. His friend, the loud one, favoured beef, so the steak in that tantalisingly secret sauce would tempt him. And it did. The third one – a smart guy, Salvatore thought — consistently selected the special, which today was chicken enchiladas in the red *mole* sauce handed down by Salvatore's grandmother. So he did. And the fourth member of the group had the homemade tortilla chips with guacamole every single weekend. This one was no different.

This evening though they brought an anomaly, a disturbance to his existence. A fifth man, exchanging repartee with the loud one. A new customer.

'And you, sir?' Salvatore leaned forward a little over the narrow counter, nodding respectfully into the man's line of vision. 'May I take your order?'

The man broke off and looked up at Salvatore, the joke lingering on his reddened cheeks as he spoke.

'I'm alright thanks, mate. I don't like Mexican.'

Salvatore recoiled; the man resumed his conversation as if nothing had happened, as if he hadn't just punched Salvatore in the gut, set fire to his kitchen and laughed in his face as it burned.

Salvatore steadied himself against this assault, palms flat on the counter as his vision briefly dissolved into static. He breathed deeply, the oxygen gradually returning to leave him feeling dizzy and a little nauseated.

'You alright, Sal?' It was the tortilla man. 'You're white as a sheet.'

Salvatore shook his head. Dislodging the last of the shock, he stood a little straighter.

'Thank you, I'm fine.' He consulted his notepad, although he knew what was on it and then looked down at his disciples.

'Four dishes. Perhaps a quesadilla for you, sir?' He forced his mouth into something of a smile and held eye contact with the fifth man although it hurt him to do so. They took his comment for banter, a cheeky sales pitch, and chuckled the tension into the night air.

'Nah, it's fine.' The fifth man gestured up the street, 'I'm gonna duck into Burger King.'

Salvatore thought he had heard the worst but this second blow was an act of violence, akin to dragging his dear grandmother from her bed and kicking her into the gutter like a dog. He turned away to conceal his shock and disgust, preparing their food as quickly as he could. He forgot to top the tacos with lime juice and the chicken went without its coriander, and he barely took the time to receive their money, so eager was he to see them gone.

The rest of his shift passed by in a blur and it was only when he locked the door and sank his chin down into his scarf that he was able to reflect. As usual he had been busy, the post-pub and pre-club crowds keeping him on his feet which, only now he was walking, started to pinch and sting. They had all been happy; dozens of people, maybe a hundred on this early winter night, eating up his chilli and finishing off the fish and begging for the secret to his steak which he would take with him to his grave. Everyone had been happy — everyone except that one man.

He screwed up his face in disgust, consumed by the memory. To not even try something: had he, Salvatore Garcia Perez, not tried everything put in front of him and more besides? Was that not the heart of his greatness in the kitchen? He thought this as one would consider the rotation of the Earth around the Sun: it was a simple fact, not a source of either modesty or pride. By the time the night bus had dropped him at the end of his quiet road, he had resolved to use his talents to educate this man, to open his eyes and his stomach to the beauty of Mexican cuisine. He was not to be feared, but pitied; not shunned, but embraced. Burrowed into the warmth of his bed twenty minutes later, he fell asleep with a small neat smile on his face.

That smile had moulded into thin-lipped concentration when the next morning found him bookmarking pages in recipe books and writing notes on a small pink pad. A creak of the floorboards above signalled that Paul was out of bed but Salvatore could hear no further than the hiss of steak searing in the pan and that peculiarly muffled crunch of a perfectly sharp knife slicing down through a bunch of fresh herbs. Paul, tying the cord of his dressing gown and breathing heavily after clattering down the stairs, had as much impact on Salvatore as the dog barking down the road.

'I was worried sick!' Paul's slippers slapped on the bare boards as he crossed to the heavy oak table. 'I had no idea if you'd been home when I woke up!'

A finger holding a line in one of the books, Salvatore looked up from the kitchen in his head, 'I couldn't sleep when there was so much work to do.' He made a note: a handful of chopped walnuts.

'So busy you haven't even made coffee?' Paul carried on into the kitchen and picked up the cold kettle, 'I'll make one, shall I?'

'No, coffee wouldn't go with this *mole*.' Salvatore added the dark chocolate and experimented with four different types of chillies. Yes — all four must be included. His grandmother would have used prunes but Salvatore felt only pomegranate molasses would do. This would win over the Englishman. Satisfied with the addition of cloves, he called out to Paul. '*Mole poblano* for dinner tonight?'

It had, Salvatore had to admit by the time the following weekend arrived, been a difficult few days. On the Wednesday, Paul had expressed his dismay at having *mole poblano* for dinner again; on the Thursday that dismay had taken the form of a large takeaway pizza, which he had silently eaten in front of Salvatore. On Friday, he took delivery of an Indian set meal, for one. But it had been worth it; Salvatore knew in his stomach that this was a flawless dish.

Saturday evening arrived on a waft of chipotle. By ten the *mole* had simmered its way to perfection and Salvatore doled out roasted squash and tortilla soup with an eye always to the street, jealously guarding the pot of darkly rich stew. Finally he spotted the bearded one and then his friends, all under-dressed for this inhospitable British weather.

The sudden flip in his stomach reminded Salvatore of the first time he had made quesadilla for Paul. He had diced chorizo and mixed it with thyme and bound it all together in cheese that melted into an extravagant embrace. He remembered clearly the dark orange oil from the meat escaping down Paul's chin, and how they had laughed at that, under the Mexican sun, Paul's skin had turned the same colour. Salvatore had enormous respect for the power of food: it had carried him here from the other side of the world.

And now these men were crossing to his side of the road, shoulders hunched against the thin drizzle. They would need warming food and Salvatore would provide.

Tonight the tortilla soup was popular and its final serving ended up in the possession of the smart one. The other three knew what they liked and were happy with that and since what they liked came from the kitchen of Salvatore, he in turn was happy with that.

So they took black bean chilli, the fish with the mango and jalapeño salsa, and the homemade tortilla chips with guacamole. The cardboard boxes were filled with steaming food and folded shut with a quick flick of the tab, then handed down. The cash came back up, to be briefly but delicately transferred into the till by hands that knew what real value was.

The fifth man stood, as last week, off to one side, half in the light of the street lamp. Hands in his pockets against the cold, he looked like a reasonable man; to a stranger, a nice man. Salvatore knew this could not be true, but even so respected his duty. Aware of the great power fizzing suddenly in his arms, Salvatore leaned forward through the hatch.

'Good evening, sir', Salvatore began. At first the man didn't realise he was being addressed, until the bearded one nudged him. The ensuing mutual embarrassment created two sets of blushing cheeks and a connection was made.

Salvatore was determined to face this evil and win. 'I have a special dish here I thought you might like to try.' His armpits bloomed with damp warmth.

'Has it got chillies in it?'

'Of course.' Salvatore spoke with authority. '*Ancho* and *mulato* chillies for sweetness, *pasilla* chilli for earthiness, and *chipotle* for smokiness. All this is complemented by the complex tones of dark chocolate and star anise, balanced by the savoury and sweet notes from —'

'Sorry mate, I don't like hot food.'

If the man had slapped Salvatore, it would have stung less. Instead he had put a match under the stock pot and cackled wildly as it boiled dry, then split in two. And they all laughed, yes, even the smart one, the tension and the connection shattered.

Amid the debris stood Salvatore, suddenly feeling the weight of the floor under his feet, as the night air cooled the perspiration decorating his forehead. He held his mouth in a rictus smile until the muscles burned long after they had left.

He was barely aware of serving the rest of the queue, his mind following that man into whichever miserable pit he laid his bones. He had failed. The *mole* sat on the stove bubbling in gentle rebuke. It seemed too sordid to take money for it, and he certainly couldn't offer it to Paul, so he gave a portion away to each remaining customer until the pan was scraped clean.

'How did it go?'

The soft voice was familiar and just for a second Salvatore couldn't place it. His face crumpled as he met Paul's eyes.

'He didn't even taste it?'

The incredulity in his voice tickled the rawness in Salvatore's heart and he sobbed, once, before regaining control.

'He did not.'

'Then he's an idiot. Your chorizo quesadilla is the best thing I've ever eaten.'

A single tear slid down Salvatore's cheek. He held himself as tall as he could. 'Then I shall make you one and then perhaps I think I will close early this evening.'

They tidied the kitchen while the cheese melted and then strolled to the bus stop together, a line of orange oil running down from Paul's smile. ✖

28 In praise of rebels
Megan Sherman

Consider Socrates, sauntering through Athens
Testing his thoughts and his tales on the throngs
And think of the first moment of perfect insight
they had. From this guru who'd made reason his song!
There in the crowd balanced wisdom and madness
But there were those who were raged by a rebellious creed
Thinking of innocent youth, corrupted with gladness
They fought to bring Socrates to death for his deeds
that threatened the state. All admire her name!
Athens collapses into panic. The jury assembles
To decide whether Socrates is to blame
For the corrupted thing the youth resembles
See the lawmakers bring justice to her knees
As they choose Hemlock for Socrates. ✖

29 Spectators
Matt West

The skipper takes to the tannoy
his bass-heavy voice,
ballasted with gravel
navigates our attention to clumsy
looking vessels

little boats — with cracked paint and
rusting hulls —
unlikely heroes that once formed part
of a flotilla
evacuating soldiers from Dunkirk
beaches in 1940.

The craft carrying us came from the
Canberra,
a blind spectator in the Falklands War,
Thatcher's iron fist, the rule of
Britannia
smashing over the Atlantic and
returning home

to pleasure-craft flocking around the
Isle of Wight,

fog horns blaring and flares casting light
on an afternoon sky as flag-waving crowds lined the shores and docks of Southampton.

But Lymington River isn't done with us yet.
A boy in the bow starts screaming with laughter as the boat hits a wave and water breaks, leaving home soaking wet. ✖

30 The crimson horror
George Pugh

This beast I see before myself
Shrouded in scarlet red
With its crimson blades overlapped
To form its graceful head.

On all sides sharp claws surround its
Neck. As creatures crawl down
They fall into its trap, left limp
And lifeless on the ground.
Though beauty always perseveres
Or acts as a disguise
This untameable terror is
Sublime we can't deny.

Look past the horror and the fear
Through its petals we see

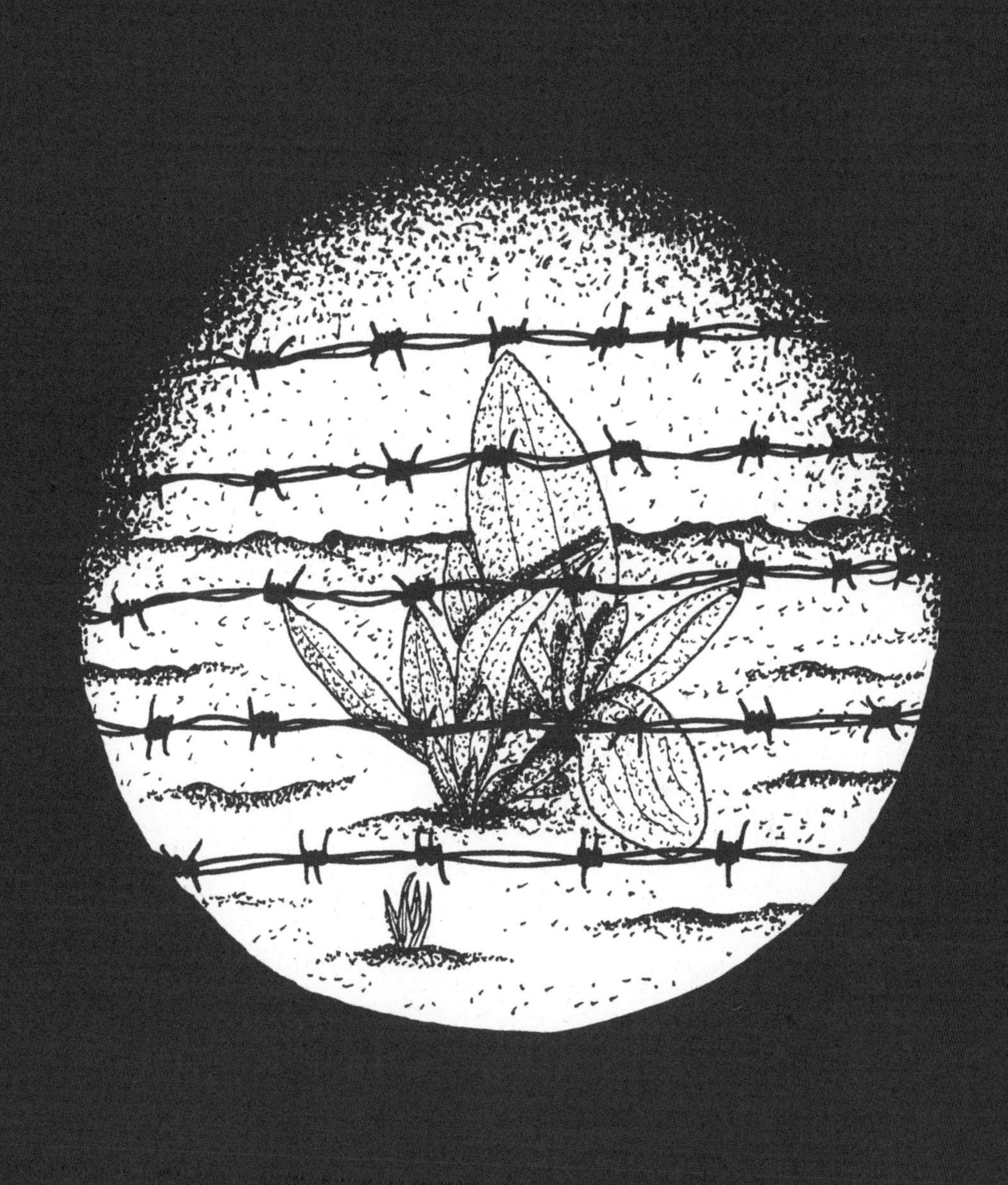

Golden shores and infinite joy;
A brief glimpse of eternity. ✖

31 From its source
Sophie Mitchell

When it is angry, it makes a loud rushing sound.
White horses rise and bolt forward, whinny and bray.
Other days it is calm, content and quiet.
White horses disappear, leaving ripples in their place.

It can carry men from where they came,
To new mountains smoothly
Or crush them as it pleases
With terrifying ease.

On sunny days it shall act as a mirror,
And show a person's life reflected in its eye.
On cloudy days it is frowned at,
And cursed, as women dart about with hats on.

Life cannot survive without it,
And yet it has the power to kill.
Whilst it should be feared and respected,
Some love it still. ✖

32 Southampton, Austen and Shakespeare
Rachel Di Nucci

Southampton has been an important port for England with visitors leaving to and entering from Europe for centuries. The city has hosted important historical figures and fictional characters have followed after their footsteps.

Jane Austen, one of the most well known writers of the last 200 years was born in Hampshire. Her eighteenth birthday, in 1793, was celebrated at the Dolphin Hotel. Southampton was also the background for some of the most vulnerable parts of her life. Austen returned to live in Southampton from 1806 to 1809 after her father died and her family were unable to stay in Bath. Once again, Austen and her sister Cassandra visited the Dolphin Hotel for dances.

The Dolphin Hotel is on the High Street. You can still sleep there. There are also some Georgian era houses near the Law Courts, between Bedford Place and London Road, which remain after air raids from World War II.

William Shakespeare also has connections with the coastal city. His patron and rumoured lover was Henry Wriothesley, 3rd Earl of Southampton. Shakespeare dedicated two of his poems to Wriothesley: 'Venus and Adonis' in 1593 and 'The Rape of Lucrece' in 1594.

The first act of *Henry V* is set in London. In the prologue of Act Two the play's background changes to Southampton where Henry and his troops set of to Agincourt from the docks. We are told as much when the Chorus declares 'The king is set from London, and the scene is now transported, gentles, to Southampton.' ×

33 A break in routine
Sian Phillips

'Can't eat these, Mer.'

Tony had grunted, using the cutlery to push the offending item — namely a portion of garden peas — around his plate aimlessly. 'They're like bloody bullets.'

That had been the comment. The one that had done it. Meryl had listened patiently as Tony critiqued the consistency of the mashed potato, the toughness of the meat and the inadequate temperature of the food that had met his lips, but it had been the gruff dismissal of the final item on the plate which had pushed her over the edge.

She had never thought a kitchen fork would be her weapon of choice, or indeed, such an effective one. She marvelled at it as she sat next to a now silent Tony at the kitchen table. Small, inauspicious; just a simple metal fork with the standard four prongs. Prongs that to any who might be so inclined to examine it were not particularly sharp, no matter how much you poked and prodded at them. Prongs now invisible to Meryl's eye, due to how deeply embedded they were in

Tony's neck. It had been the spray of blood that had caused her to audibly gasp; an arterial fountain that had not only hit Meryl, but the surrounding units that housed all of their kitchen utensils. She licked her lips slowly and grimaced somewhat at the metallic taste that met her tongue. She used her fingers to pick at the now cold pieces of chicken on his plate and nibbled at a small piece in an attempt to take the flavour of old pennies away.

She liked Tony when he was quiet. For years she had endured his booming voice, and her ears had never failed to groan at the intrusion. This, however, was bliss. His head hung limply over the table; he was slumped in the manner he would be if Manchester City were losing at home, only he wasn't shouting and spitting over the state of things. He was simply still.

Meryl sipped slowly at the coffee she had made, and hissed softly at the searing, momentary pain she felt because of the heat. The bitter taste soothed her and she relaxed somewhat when she realised she didn't have to immediately jump up to retrieve the dessert. This would typically be served on completion of their main; Tony barely took the time to wipe the remnants of his dinner from his mouth before he insisted on pudding. No more.

Meryl glanced at his face and smiled when she saw how his mouth was open somewhat, a half-formed silent shriek omitted from his lips. Part comedy and part tragedy, she surmised. It was odd how his eyes were open, but they were unfocused and glassy, reminding her of Janet Leigh in *Psycho*. A film, ironically, she'd seen at the pictures all those years ago with Tony, in their early days of courtship.

She sighed loudly. *EastEnders* was on. She could hear the muffled voices from the television in the other room. Usually she'd shuffle in to watch it after spooning their dessert into bowls, but not tonight. Tonight that routine had been spoiled. Instead, Meryl thought, as she clicked her tongue in an irritated fashion against her teeth, she would have to work out how to best to remove the blood stains from the soft yellow walls of the kitchen. ✖

34 Riverseed chronicles (a novel extract)
Georgia Jerrey

The ivy spun and twisted, silhouetted against the light. It reminded her of the black tar her father told stories about, sticky and full of darkness that spread over the brain, like leeches sucking out the light. She had to be strong, her father had informed her, keep the light shining so the darkness wouldn't take over. If only she could do that now but she was too late. The demons had taken over.

She was stripped of her silks, right down to the undergarments of her brown leather bodice and frail white petticoats and forced into the Night Tower of blackened stone and climbing ivy. She had nothing except a mirror and a plate of food for company. 'What is this?' Ari thought. This was not like her father, unless there was something he wasn't telling. Something to do with her mother.

The gentle pat of infant feet on the steps; up, up, up and up the tower she goes. She would own all of this one day her daddy once told her. Queen of the tower, Queen of the tower, Queen of the tower she would be, Queen of the tower for all to see.

But what did the Queen of the tower see? Her mother dealing poison with her king… and you spoke up, ran, spoke up and ran and told didn't you — just like the good little girl you are. My Father… would have died anyway, of old age or battle. But I was… just the child you are. Running and telling like a good little girl.

An arrow flew through the window:

'You need to leave Arianna. NOW, Luc'

Fall. Fall and you'll fly little girl or fall to hell. She dropped from the window, flying free once more. Onto Luc's horse.

'Oh dear God Ari!'
'Luc?'
'Yes?'
'Oh, it is you.'
'Of course. Who else would I be?'

The voice in my head, my mother.

'No one. Never mind. Just ride!'

And they galloped. ×

35 Why do I write?
Kate Freeman

To escape. To create the world I would rather live in. To build the house I dream to live in. There are so many reasons I write, I enjoy it but I want to improve too. Writing is putting your thoughts down on the page in front of you, making them real and cementing them in reality. I love knowing that someone has read my work and even more so if they understand it.

In the moment I am putting something down on paper it is all I am thinking about and nothing else matters. I am letting the words flow and fall into place, of course I might go back and edit bits but at the time I don't let mistakes stop me. Escapism is a wonderful thing, the getting away from whatever is worrying you and letting something else occupy your mind entirely. That's the beauty of it. When I am writing I feel completely different; I can feel the pathways in my brain being exercised, bringing out the words that I might not use in everyday conversation and illuminating every option of where to go next. When my mind is not present 'in reality' it is somewhere I know that it can work better, somewhere where there are no restrictions and every creation from me is in one place.

I write for the imagination that is dying to become a reality. There are parts of me that need to not be limited by money or time. There are parts of me that die inside when I am reminded of those that I've lost but come alive again from the memory and my writing. It is extraordinary what you can feel with words, how a tear can come to your eye or you can become enraged by a silly sentence. Writing is powerful when you do it correctly. Kill the character you fell in love with creating, send away the love you wish you had done sooner and bring back the mother you never really knew. The possibilities are endless, everyone's writing is unique and why they do it is too.

The world is an amazing place as it is, miracles happen all the time and there are wonders in the world that make some speechless. Some writers have created this themselves, imagined a different world to live in entirely. I have not yet gotten to this point but it is my goal. The extent of my creation is a detailed house and a small town that hasn't got much in it. But I write to improve, I have goals and targets I will one day reach and I will do it through my own imagination growing to eventually emerge into the world I wish to live in.

I write for myself. ×

36 The fairy's tail
George Pugh

There a- re drag-
ons and demon- s in these my-
stical tales, whos- e p- ower and horror nev-
er fails. Grotesque the- mes and terrible scenes are cove-
red and hidden by illusions and dreams. Imaginings of princesses s
tuck in high towers, unable to escape f- rom the darkest of powers. V-
aliant knights riding mighty st- eeds, always at hand in the hour of n-
eed. Witches on brooms turn- ing kings in to frogs and fabled heroes make their wa-
y through the fog. Trolls u- nder bridges that bloc- k your way, the least likely g-
uy who saves the day. A- ll this morally upstand- ing detail to brighten your
eyes, and to stop you from revealing the most d- eceitful disguise. The gore b-
ehind the magic skilfully c- oncealed, so that tru- th of these stories are never r-
evealed. The house made of candy is used to hid- e, the gruesome cannibal lingering inside. They focus on Cinde- rella's foot being pl- aced in the glass slipper; instead o-
f the step-sister butchering her o- wn in the hope it m- ight fit her. The story of Rapunzel w-
ith flowing long hair, who was s- aved by her prince, all noble and fair. It's actually a tale
of despair and dread, it ends w- ith the father cutting off her head. The magical Pied Piper w-
ith his wonderful tun- es was not as wo- nderful as one might ass-
ume. He led t- he poor children a- way from their
homes to a la- nd f-
illed with pai- n, h-
ungry and al- one.
The Brothers Gri- mm
Removed th- ese d- ist- urbi-
ng de- tails and f-
ormed them in the guise of
fairy tales. ×

37 Ahab
Flavio de Oliveria

Rats with wings, they call them, but there's much more to pigeons than it appears. Trust me. I know. I know. I have looked many of them in the eye. They have their own hidden agenda, especially these that hang out at Heathrow Central Bus Station.

They have schemes, they have plans and traps, they have skills and cunning and, most of all, they have intent.

It wasn't too long ago that I first start noticing them and their… ways. Innocent creatures my feathery arse. They are clever. They manipulate the common bystander. I used to be one of those. Not too long ago, I was sitting on this very seat, waiting for my coach after a long plane trip. You know how those things are, I came in unwittingly, not knowing how long I'd have to wait for the next coach home. Home. I missed home terribly, then, before I realised where I actually was. I digress. There was a two-hour wait for the bus, and that was dreadful. If it had been… 30 minutes earlier… so much less pain, so fewer sleepless nights of wandering into town at three in the morning, bumping into drunken students stinking of cheap kebab and equally cheap beer, instinctively heading back to their student halls like ants, or more like a recreation of Pieter Bruegel the Elder's *The Parable of the Blind*. The nightmares… anyway, my stomach grumbled, it roared at me, threateningly, or should I say, chirped at me threateningly, so I bought myself a couple of packets of crisps (a naive mistake). Unbeknownst to me, their cunning plan was hatched, already in motion, the minute they had set their little impatient eyes on me. Those eyes, I can feel them right now.

Can't you?

You will, eventually. By the handful, I gorged myself with the salt and vinegar flavoured crisps (saving the grilled steak flavoured one as my main course) and gulped great amounts of lemonade to wash it all down. They watched me feast. Oh, yes, they were watching! Perched somewhere, perhaps across the street, under the seats, under the tables from Caffé Nero. I'm sure they watched me. I kept indulging myself, until the last few bits of crisps were left in the bag. You know, those tiny little specks that you need to turn the bag over your hand to get at. That's what I did. That was also the point that they assured themselves of their strategy — in my blissful ignorance, I had not realised that eating those final specks were found terribly offensive by their kind. Believe me, it is as bad as if I came into your house around dinner time, you, with your husband and kids at the table, after saying a prayer or turning on the telly, then I'd come in and just spit on your food and spill salad dressing on the steak, steak sauce on your crème brûlée, it's as bad as that. Their sustenance comes from those 'unwanted' crumbs and from their aforementioned manipulation of humans. But we'll get to that soon.

As I proceeded to finish off my entrée, I noticed some movement within my perspective. I was idle, so I gave little attention to it at first, until I noticed one of its legs. That fat, white-feathered pigeon had one deformed foot, like a clenched fist. It moved about in a limp, picking and pecking at the scraps on the floor left behind by careless commuters or, as I call them, unintentional breeders of hell birds. Its leg was horrific, I should have stopped staring at it but I couldn't. I know you wouldn't turn away either – it was like watching a car crash, or watching the paper coming out of an inkjet printer – I just had to watch it move. Another mistake, in the series of mistakes I made in dealing with their turf. Oh yes, this is their turf, this is their zone, you're on borrowed time in here if you don't watch yourself.

No, I'm not threatening you myself; I'm just warning you of them! Having finished off the first packet, I continued my self-indulgent lunch with those grilled steak crisps. I couldn't open the packet however, no matter how hard I pulled and tugged on it. I decided to use my keys to rip the bag open. As I did so, pressuring the metal key against the top of the bag, hoping to make a hole into it, the key slipped too far into the plastic, ripping it wide open, its contents flying off all around me. In my surprise and desperation, I waved my hands about like a mad peacock and my keys flew off my grip! That was the moment they were waiting for! In a quick sweep, one of their attack pigeons picked up my keys while a swarm of other smaller pigeons, obviously inserted there as decoys, attacked the crisps! I had lost my keys, my only set of keys! Panicking, I fell onto my knees, scrambling with the pecking pigeons on the floor, searching if, by chance, my keys hadn't fallen in the mess. While on my knees, my own posterior thrust into the air, another of their scouts swept by and picked my wallet out my back pocket! Their revenge was complete — I felt the pain and humiliation of being caught in a trap, a carefully and devilishly concocted trap worthy of Greek tragedies! No keys to get into my house, and no money to call a key maker.

That is why, madam, if I may call you so, I humbly ask you for any spare change. No, it's not for new keys. It is time for my own revenge; I have taken upon myself to bring these creatures to justice, my own sore hands' justice. Any penny will help, madam. Any penny at all. ✖

38 Untitled
Pam Jones

No matter the age
No matter the life

I see through water
Bright green eyes

Cry tears of water
Salty to taste

I bathe in water
Soft melting bubbles

I drink tap water
Hard and cold

I feel rainwater
Salt and earth

I float on water
In the Solent

I’m made of water
Of millions of years ✖

General Editor
Matthew Cheeseman

Editors
Jessica Bentley
Rachel Di Nucci
Josh Jones
Lottie King
Kieran O'Connor
Poppy O'Brien
Katherine Orman
William Palmer
George Pugh
Martin Tvenning

Marketing
Bobby Newton
Claudia Wilson

Illustration
Patryk Wirenski
behance.net/deepcoffeeillstrtn

Design
Go! Grafik
www.gografik.ch

Technical student support
Tom Fowler

Subbing
Aaron Thompson

Thanks to
Suzanne Dixon, Solent Creatives and everyone who submitted work. Extra special thanks go to Innocents Size.

This book is dedicated to everyone who submitted their work or supported us in any way. This one's for you.

This volume produced by students working with Solent Press at Southampton Solent University. The views expressed are the contributors' own and as such the University and its staff can not be held responsible.

Paper	Cyclus offset
Printing	Graphius / New Goff
Edition	600 copies

First published in the United Kingdom in 2017 by Solent Press. Printed on recycled paper with vegan ink.

Solent Press is a cost-effective content and publishing agency. We combine industry expertise with student creativity to produce compelling words, images and designs.

We know how to tell a story so that people take notice. From social media and blog entries to complete books and magazines in print or digital, we have a solution to your communication needs.

We're staffed by talented students so can offer an energy and insight that other agencies just can't match. Our objective is to give students great professional experience whilst making content affordable to you, so we're extremely cost-effective.

A team of experienced editors and designers oversee the day-to-day running of Solent Press, ensuring everything is done to a professional standard. Speak with one of our full-time professional staff to discover how Solent Press can help you to reach your audience.

Invest in the writers of tomorrow, discover new talent and make fruitful connections within Southampton Solent University.

solentpress.info

SOLENTPRESS
Digital and print solutions

ISBN: 978-0-907426-46-2